GW00399872

Gone to Ground

Illustrated and written by
Jessica Perry

Weather or not,
the year begins here...

Worms
settle down and
centipedes cease running
as Mole listens for lingering
creaks downstairs. Dry, cold
woodlice tonight, with just a
chance of an isolated spider
during the early hours.
4°

Tonight
will see rummaging,
followed by dry cider and
cheesecakes over the weekend,
leading to peppermints in the
early hours, and hazy conditions.
Mist and fog are slow to lift, but
mild winter sunshine can
be expected.
7°

Weather
balloon forecasts
present risks of mist
opportunities. A band may
breeze in during the early
hours, showering crumbs and
fiddling with the toaster
settings.
3°

Tonight,
Eunice blows off
with blustery blasts, pops
out in her slippers, skids on a
south westerly and throws down
an old oak outside the pub.
Easing a touch overnight, but
muttering threats.
5 °

Heavy
rain ends a long
day, which continues to
stretch into evening. Coil pots
develop through the night but
lose their identity, despite best
intentions. Odd, windy, and
with ominous tendencies.
12°

Drier
indoors, with an
outside risk of hail, snow
and sunshine. A breezy manner
with moderately flamboyant
tendencies, bordering on peculiar.
Tonight, will see knitting with
worms, with some stocking
stitch in places.
5°

Tonight,
there will be
muffled chaos with little
success and diminishing
returns. Long, dark spells
in odd places with no
apparent solutions.
7°

Scattered
condiments continue,
but with persistent shaking
some ketchup will appear.
A mild night for
some . . .
7°

Tonight,
overcoats turn into
blankets: dry at first, with
hot water bottles later. Rain
and sleet fall downwards with snow
over the molehills. There may be a
few bare ankles, with snow and sleet
accumulations in the wheelbarrow.
Windy, but not as cold by the
fireplace.
5°

Some
crowded corridors
and an unexpected visitor
by nightfall. It will turn
increasingly loud overhead,
with shelter possible in
odd spots.
7°

This
evening will see
nothing, as it's all dark.
Extensive belt tightening, with
just the odd wintry blast up the
dressing gown. Smoke drifting in
at times, most likely from
the fireplace.
3°

This
evening would
see plenty of sky if
it wasn't so dark. Clouds
increase with cold breezes in
tunnels, offering temporary
shelter and a hazelnut in
shared chambers.
11°

Blustery
showers will
stream in overnight,
heavy at times, with crowds
of predators banging on
the ceiling.
10°

This
evening, crowds
linger below with
belongings in bags. Clear
rain falls from the sky, gradually
filling the water butt overnight.
Worms continue at
full stretch.
9°

A cold night
pulling out all the stops
with thoughts of Spring and
harmoniums. Bright and gusty,
with scatter cushions and no
table manners. Mild and
breezy. Slightly cheesy.
3°

Urgence
and persistence,
moving onwards and
upwards through the aconite,
emerging with occasional toads
in the hole. Underground
shelters will open as
conditions allow.
8°

There
will be heavy
petting in moist areas,
long into the night as rain falls
downwards. Overnight, slippers
will be tossed sideways and it
will turn chilly without

pyjamas.
10°

Remaining
dry and cold, with
shelter under brambles.
Low clouds push in from the
early hours, merging moistly
and settling down with
damp frogs.
8°

This
evening, the
chambers resonate yet
again with The Archers Morse
code: Dum di dum di dum di dum,
dum di dum di daaa da. Da di da
di da di dit, da di diddley da.
Dawn is lingering on the stairs,
with odd spots of drizzle
on her nightie.
17°

There
is a chance of
capture, with some missed,
some mourning, and the fog
of war developing. Under these
skies, quiet munching and scurrying
continues. It will be a little
chilly, with dynamite
in places.
10°

Tonight
hears the upward
creak of bluebells, as
wintry showers from the
north scatter above ground.
Worms respond and resist
accordingly.
4°

Northwesterly
gales form tribute
bands, performing loud songs
across the country throughout
the daytime. Eventually, they
will clear off into the night after
little applause. Turning quite
frosty towards Dawn.
7°

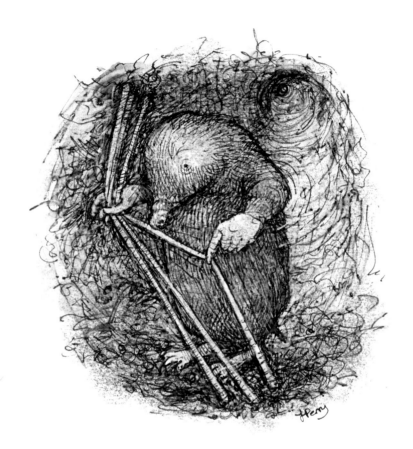

44

Remaining
cloudy and cool,
with dirty plates left till
morning. Tending to linger
longer overnight, with the
odd breakage possible
in places.
8°

Tonight,
clouds fade away and
skies turn large and clear.
In the early hours, a few areas
of doubt develop as, once again,
the wrong end of the stick has
been grasped. It will remain
difficult with a westerly
wheeze.
14°

Tonight
may feel persistently
cold if doors continue to be
left open. The chance of a light mac
is followed by a dark brown overcoat.
Bright and breezy, whilst long periods
of prevarication continue throughout
the week. Clowns sweeping in from
the north will honk horns
throughout.
10°

Lingering
largely in daywear
with variable smells in places.
There may be the odd spot of
lemon drizzle around the back of the
fridge, becoming larger on Sunday.
Sharp elbows pushing in from the
north, and some bright spark
appearing later in the day
to clear up the mess.
$19°$

Variable clouds
of pipe-smoke waft out
from the chamber overnight.
Slippers remain by the bed as
it continues to be a cool,
quiet night in.
10°

This
evening will see
a few larvae getting under
one's feet in one's personal
chamber. Low humming and some
nasal whistling will persist, with
a right shower expected to
emerge tomorrow.
14°

Tonight
continues all over
the place in as many ways
as ever, with dry skies through
the first part. Early hours, a few
uninterested clouds drift by
from up north, but they will be
dry ones. Hot sun and high
pressure ahead
20°

Exceptionally
hot. Temperatures
mid-to-high thirties, with
some places in the forties. Plenty
of sunshine, shandy, light burping
and wind. Heavy showers and
thunderstorms anticipated keenly.
Pyjamas not necessary. At all.
Ever again.
35°

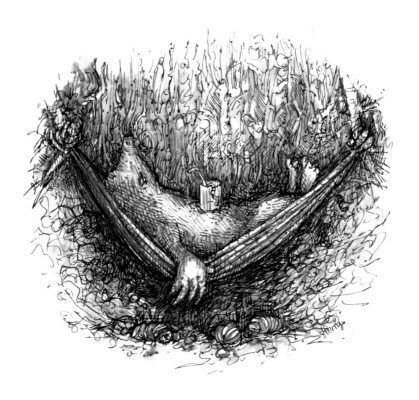

Today's
emerging   nose
will sense a cloudy start
with a few droplets. Warm
sunny spells lead to a muggy
night with flitting bats
overhead. Staying dry,
turning breezier.
24°

Showers
and baths have
ceased, leaving a sink wash
for the foreseeable. Duvets are
variable with windbreaks, missing
buttons and some damp patches. Odd
spots of levity, but extensive housing
developing for the rest. Saturday
looks to be another Sunday,
with more likely.
19°

Tonight,
widespread showers
lead to damp towels and a
full bucket. The odd toad with
spots is expected, as are the
rumblings of Big Hedgehog.
Rainbow chard will develop
overnight.
17°

Showers
ease and a chance
of mushrooms develop across
many fields. Thumps and creaks
likely as variable fungi emerge, but
it will remain largely clear with
vests on. Gusty winds near
the back door.
16°

Tonight
could see a pint of
cider with peanuts at times.
Consequently, tomorrow will be
very windy, with some surprising
gusts. Woodlice arrive around
midday, with rain and slugs
clearing the dishes later.
17°

Dry
observations and
cloud-building continues.
Local heavies move in during
the early hours: wheeled suitcases
thudding up the stairs without
so much as a by-your-leave.
Blustering gussets expected
later in the week.
12°

Clouds
spread upstairs as
potatoes come to the
boil. Spatters of tomato sauce
turn drier overnight, with a
few left-over sausages by
tomorrow. Mild, with
critical tendencies.
14°

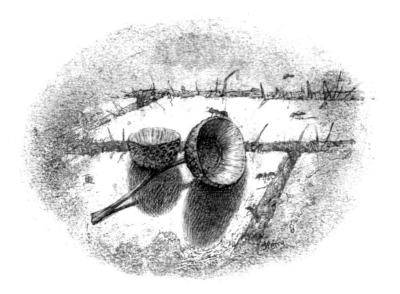

Heavy
rain, with further
buckets of thunder
expected. Despite 15-togs,
socks and additional hot water
bottles, sluggish conditions
persist, with soup, followed by
unintended consequences.
Red cabbage ahead.
12°

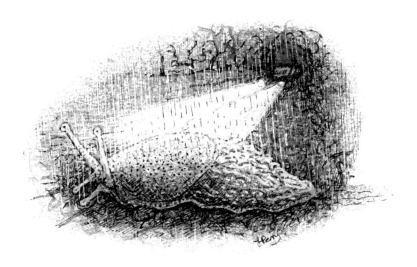

Grass
ceilings combine
with brick walls, leading
to odd spots and few sunny
spells. Stretching onwards and
sideways, finding a dark place by
midday. Wet and windy showers
likely, with drifting rain
and empty buses.
9°

Fog,
mist and wood-
smoke expected, leading
to slow-moving traffic and
emerging tussocks. Odd socks
cannot be ruled out, with
long-john's expected later.
Spells of rain, heavy
at times.
8°

Skies
will be large
this evening, with more
potatoes. Areas of cloud from
the vest will push on into the
second half of the pyjamas. It
will turn rather wet, leading
to Brussels sprouts later
in the week.
8°

Tonight,
it will be dark with
clear silence for much
of the evening. However,
slumber will develop as sheep
encroach, pushing dreams
onwards until morning.

6°